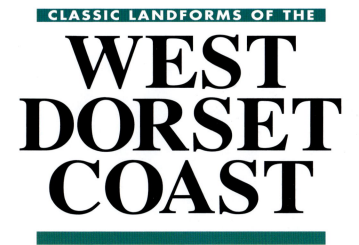

CLASSIC LANDFORMS OF THE

WEST DORSET COAST

Robert Allison, Ken Coombe, Roger Moore, Alex Koh and Helen Rudkin have been stimulating research students who have added greatly to our knowledge of this coast; and Mark Lee has been an inspirational enthusiast. This new edition is dedicated to them all. *Denys Brunsden and Andrew Goudie*

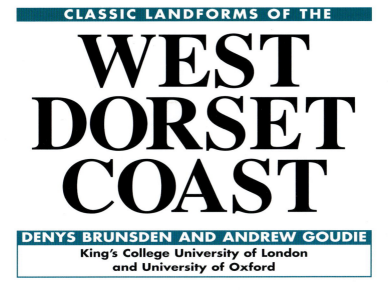

CLASSIC LANDFORMS OF THE

WEST DORSET COAST

DENYS BRUNSDEN AND ANDREW GOUDIE
King's College University of London
and University of Oxford

Series editors
Rodney Castleden and Christopher Green

Published by the Geographical Association
in conjunction with the
British Geomorphological Research Group

THE GEOGRAPHICAL ASSOCIATION

PREFACE

Geomorphologists study landforms and the processes that create and modify them. The results of their work, published as they invariably are in specialist journals, usually remain inaccessible to the general public. We would like to put that right. Scattered across the landscapes of England and Wales there are many beautiful and striking landforms that delight the eye of the general public and are also visited by educational parties from schools, colleges and universities. Our aim in producing this series of guides is to make modern explanations of these classic landforms available to all, in a style and format that will be easy to use in the field. We hope that an informed understanding of the origins of the features will help the visitor to enjoy the landscape all the more.

Encouraged by the success of the first edition of the Classic Landform Guides we are pleased to introduce this new edition, enhanced by colour photographs, new illustrations and with the valuable addition of 1:50 000 map extracts by kind permission of the Education Team, Ordnance Survey. The relevant maps for the area covered in this booklet are the Ordnance Survey 1:50 000 Landranger sheets 193 and 194; please refer to the current Ordnance Survey Index for 1:25 000 availability.

Rodney Castleden *Roedean School, Brighton*
Christopher Green *Royal Holloway, University of London*

Acknowledgements

We would like to acknowledge the friendship, advice and information received over the years, notably from Alan Carr, David K.C. Jones, David Horsfall and Geoff Poole. The work of the British Geological Survey, Bernard Conway and Bruce Denness, has proved particularly useful in the account of Higher Sea Lane, as has that of Malcolm Bray for beach sediment fluxes.

Over the years, Roma Beaumont and Gordon Reynall have been wonderful and willing cartographers, and we also thank the cartographers of the School of Geography at Oxford, Peter Hayward and Ailsa Allen, for drawing the original versions of the illustrations. We also thank the many students we have taken to the area for their hard work and penetrating questions, and the Carlton Hotel, Weymouth and the Bull Hotel, Bridport under the Terleski family for their superb hospitality.

Denys Brunsden and Andrew Goudie

CONTENTS

Safety

The coast, can be very dangerous both because the cliffs are subject to rockfalls and because the mudslides and mudflows are very deep and do not support one's weight. Notice and heed the warning notices at Black Ven and avoid the central parts of Stonebarrow or wherever you see bare, wet muds.

Cover photograph: The Cobb, Lyme Regis. *Photo:* Sillson Communications, Wareham.
Frontispiece: The Spittles landslides, February 1987,
Photo: Denys Brunsden.
Acknowledgements
The Geographical Association would like to thank those individuals and organisations referred to in figure captions for their permission to reproduce illustrations in this publication:
Mapping reproduced from Ordnance Survey 1:50 00 Landranger mapping with permission of The Controller of Her Majesty's Stationery Office © Crown Copyright 82324M 09/96
Copy Editing: Kath Davies
Illustrations: Paul Coles
Series design concept: Quarto Design, Huddersfield
Design and typesetting: Armitage Typo/Graphics, Huddersfield
Printed and bound in Hong Kong by: Colorcraft Limited

INTRODUCTION

The Dorset coast, which is one of the most beautiful and spectacular coastlines in the world, is also of remarkable scientific importance to geologists and to those who study landforms – geomorphologists. For those people interested in landscape, the coast is perhaps best known for its variety of rocks and famous fossil localities, but visitors are invariably struck by the equally impressive though not so widely explained coastal landforms, which display many striking contrasts and obvious evidence of active processes of erosion and deposition.

The purpose of this guide is therefore to provide a concise description and explanation of some of the most important of these features in west Dorset, between Lyme Regis and Portland Bill. The companion publication *Classic Landforms of the East Dorset Coast* looks at the Dorset Coast between the Isle of Portland and Poole Harbour. We have chosen to look particularly at a group of actively collapsing cliffs – Black Ven, Stonebarrow and Golden Cap – and their relationship to the remarkable Chesil Beach. These localities are all characterised by episodic marine erosion and cliff retreat, seasonal movement of mud and complex patterns of landslide activity. We are able in this account to look in some detail at the recent history of their development and to trace the sediment they supply to the Lyme Bay sediment cell.

We look at the problem of living alongside this dynamic landscape. We consider the consequences of disturbing the natural landscape and the natural rhythm of coastal processes, and comment on the management solutions that have evolved in response to the problems.

THE MOVING CLIFFS OF WEST DORSET

The coastal cliffs of west Dorset (Figure 1) owe their shape to the relief and orientation of the coastline, the variable properties or **lithology** of the rocks, the geological structure, the history of relative land and sea movements, the sequences of environmental change, the difference in erosional energy of the sea between the more exposed and sheltered parts of Lyme Bay, and to the complex sub-aerial processes which currently act on the cliffs themselves.

The orientation of the coastline

The first important landform control is that the coastline runs approximately west to east in an asymmetrical bay from Lyme Regis to West Bay. Four narrow ridges terminate at the sea in spectacular cliffs which are the highest on the south coast of England, reaching 191m at Golden Cap. These cliffs are the locations of some

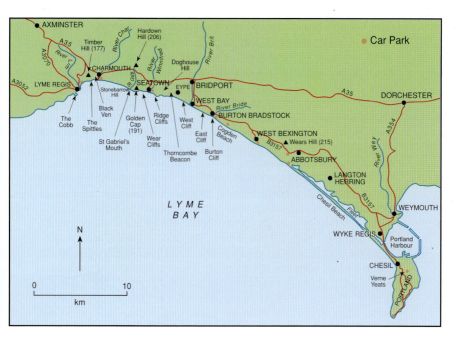

Figure 1: The topography of the west Dorset coast. From Brunsden and Goudie 1981, and Allison 1992.

of the most dynamic landforms in Britain. At Timber Hill, just to the east of Lyme Regis, are the active mudslides of the Spittles and Black Ven, over 150m high (see pages 23-27). Where Stonebarrow Down reaches the sea the cliffs consist of rotational landslides, mudslides and toppling cliffs, parts of which are sometimes called Cain's Folly and Fairy Dell. An extension of Hardown Hill forms the near vertical cliffs of Golden Cap, and Eype Down yields the lovely sea views from Doghouse Hill and Thorncombe Beacon.

Between these ridges, only the valleys of the Lim, Char and Brit rivers form systems fully adjusted to base level. Smaller streams like the Winnaford and Eype brooks have just reached sea-level whilst Westhay Water, Ridge Water, St Gabriel's Water and several dry valleys hang above the beach because they are unable to keep pace with the rapid rate of coastal cliff retreat. Between Charmouth, Seatown and Eype there are, therefore, low but steep cliffs marked successively by waterfalls from the elevated streams, or cascades of mud from small but interesting landslides. One of the most instructive 'landslide walks' in Britain lies between Stonebarrow and Golden Cap because the forms are so varied.

The second important landform control is the nature of the different beds of rock, deposited millions of years ago in geological time (Table 1). The headlands with which we are concerned generally consist of a thick capping of sandy sediments of Lower Cretaceous age (c.130 million years old) (see Table 1 and Figure 2).

The younger **Cherts** and the Upper Greensand are permeable and form steep slopes at the tops of the sea cliffs. These slopes generally fail by gradual slumps, sudden rotational landslides and occasionally, when very wet, by sand flows. The older underlying clays are often fissured and softened to depths of 1-2m and are easily eroded by gullies, mudslides and rotational slips. The seaward cliffs collapse in rockfalls and toppling slabs and are also dissected by gullies. The limestone bands within the clays often form more resistant layers or beds, giving rise to shallow benches in the cliff profile over which the mudslides move. The Belemnite Beds are of particular importance in controlling the steepness and erosion rate of the cliffs, forming a vertical undercliff in the middle of Black Ven, a vertical sea cliff at Stonebarrow and a basal zone of erosion resistance at the foot of Golden Cap.

The differing geomorphological behaviour of these rocks can be related to their physical properties. The close-jointed Cherts readily break up to form angular, rocky debris. The Upper Greensand and the Gault contain particles of extremely fine sands and silts which are only lightly cemented together but possess quite a high frictional strength. Because both are permeable they can stand at quite a steep angle. Their behaviour when wet owes much to the collapse of the 'loose' or unconsolidated structure. In Dorset, workmen digging trenches in this material are wary of what they call 'running sand'.

Table 1: Summary of the stratigraphy

Name and age	Nature of rock	Maximum thickness	Locality (see Figure 1)	Behaviour
Lower Cretaceous				
Chert	Closely jointed hard siliceous	9m	Black Ven	Breaks up into coarse gravel, forms same, and main beach supply
Upper Greensand (Foxmould)	Yellow, orange, silty fine sand	30m	Stonebarrow Golden Cap	Permeable but can flow. When drained can form steep angles on upper slopes
Gault	Green grey silts and clays	5-15m	Golden Cap Stonebarrow Black Ven	Causes landslides, acts as aquiclude
Middle Jurassic				
Forest Marble	Clay and shelly limestone	25m	West Cliff	Forms a thin cap-rock and minor hills
Fuller's Earth	Clay with thin limestone	45m	West Cliff	Very unstable. Famous landslide at West Bay
Inferior Oolite	Hard shelly limestone	6m	East Cliff, West Bay, Burton Bradstock	Usually a thin cap-rock
Upper Lias				
Bridport Sands	Soft sandstones with harder beds	49m	Various locations, Seatown to Burton Bradstock	Well drained forms main hillslopes near Bridport
Downcliff Clay	Clay	21m	Golden Cap to Eype	Causes minor sliding on coast
Middle Lias				
Thorncombe Sands	Soft sandstones	21m	Seatown to Eype	Forms steep cliffs, fails in shallow
Downcliff Sands	Soft sands	30m	Golden Cap to Eype	Slides of planar type
Eype Clay	Clays and sandstones	60m	Stonebarrow to West Cliff	Unstable cliffs, rapid erosion
Three Tiers	Silty sand with hard sandstone bands	9m	Stonebarrow to Seatown	Forms undercliff and rotational landslides
Lower Lias				
Green Ammonite Beds	Clays and limestones	32m	Black Ven to Seatown	Vertical sea cliffs and landslide units.
Belemnite Marls	Hard mudstones	23m	Black Ven to Golden Cap	Belemnite Stone more cemented, limestones cause benches in profile.
Black Ven Marls	Clays and thin limestones	46m	Black Ven to Stonebarrow	
Shales with Beef	Clays and thin limestones	21m	Black Ven	Failure surfaces common in shales.
Blue Lias	Clays and thin limestones	32m	Black Ven	Blue Lias forms steep cliffs.

The clays and silts readily absorb water and soften to a very sticky and slippery consistency so that layers can easily split or shear over one another to start mudslides on steep slopes. With a lot of water they may even flow like avalanches of liquid mud.

The structure of the rocks

Another important control on the processes of the area is the structural attitude of the rocks (Figure 2). The **Mesozoic** and **Tertiary** strata of west Dorset have been gently folded in both the mid-Cretaceous and the Tertiary. There is evidence that the north-west/south-east structures in the basement still exert a landforming influence and that some of the folds may be draped over underlying block structures. In west Dorset most of the folds are very gentle. The main structure is the Marshwood Dome or **pericline** which lies to the north of the coastline. This imparts a 2-3°, east-south-east dip to the Lower Lias rocks. The overlying Upper Greensand and Gault rest **unconformably** and almost horizontally on the clays.

Behind and under Chesil Beach the important Ridgeway Fault and the Weymouth Anticline bring a full Jurassic sequence to the surface and this yields a more gentle but varied 'coastal' relief. There are minor faults in the cliff exposures and a famous complicated system at Fault Corner, Eype and Bridport. These affect water movement and the location and form of landslides or gullies. The main structural influence, however, is the dip of the rocks. This leads water along the **aquiclude** toward the eroding sea cliffs and creates the classic landslide situation of permeable rocks overlying impermeable materials. This old principle of landsliding has been recently called 'the reservoir principle'.

Changes in the levels of land and sea

It is not known to what extent the area has been uplifted since the Tertiary movements. It is likely that the individual basement blocks have continued to adjust slowly but there does not seem to have been much change in elevation or tilting. The latest calculations and surveyed measurements show that west Dorset is a relatively stable area (Figure 3a).

Sea-level is a much more fundamental control because it is the base level for erosional systems, coastal processes and river development.

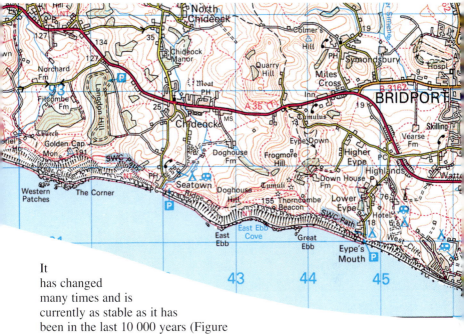

It
has changed
many times and is
currently as stable as it has
been in the last 10 000 years (Figure
3c). Relict landslides, buried channels and submerged
forests, such as those in the valley and mouth of the River Char, are
a dominant feature. The coast is obviously vulnerable to such changes
and the Dorset coast cannot be understood except in terms of sea-level
change. The rising sea, after the last glacial episode, probably reached
the predecessors of the present cliffs c.5000 years ago and the
evidence of the drowned landslides at Golden Cap and the profiles of
the hanging rivers is that, in some places, this may have occurred as
much as 4km offshore (Bray 1992). This yields an erosion figure
similar to the current coastal erosion rates of 0.6m per year. This
cannot, however, have been the case along the whole coast;
for example, very old, degraded and uneroded cliffs persist behind
Chesil Beach. The current sea-level rise in Dorset is no more than
1-2mm/year and may be less (Figure 3b).

Environmental changes

Long-term environmental changes have also had a pronounced
effect on the development of the west Dorset landscape. One of
the most impressive features of the area is the fine summit surface that
presents a level skyline from every hilltop. The highest hills reach a
common level c.200+m and may represent the dissected remnants of
a slightly deformed landsurface, sloping south-southeast away from
the Marshwood Vale pericline and from which the current drainage
pattern has partially evolved. At Black Down the surface is capped by
Chert and flint gravels, of Middle Eocene age, including rare Budleigh
Salterton quartzites derived from the west. Similar gravels occur at

Eggardon Hill and Pilsdon Pen. Even on slightly lower hills, such as Stonebarrow, remnants of such gravels survive in the ancient soils. It is believed that this surface represents an Early Tertiary land surface partly transgressed by the Eocene Sea. In fact, the deposits on the surface vary in age by as much as 10 million years and are polygenetic in origin.

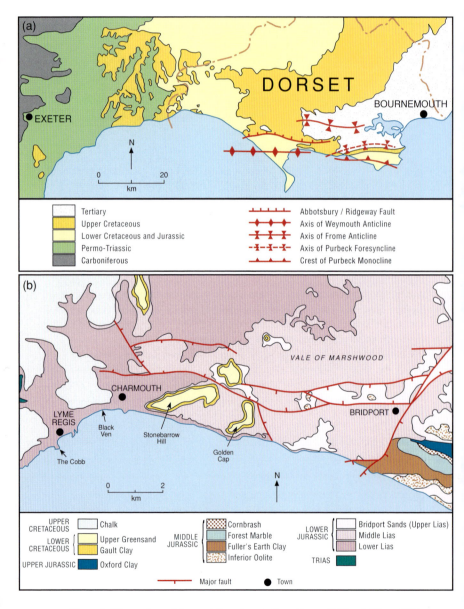

Figure 2: The geology of the west Dorset coast. *From House 1989 and Allison 1992.*

Two other deposits are of particular note. The edges of the surface close to some of the valleys appear to have developed **silcretes** or **sarsens**. These are now found in the bottom of dry valleys such as the Valley of the Stones near Portesham and no longer on the preserved remnants of the original surface. They were once part of the soil cover of the ancient surface and formed when the climate was warm (seasonal-tropical), much like parts of southern Africa today.

This idea is supported by studies of the residual soils on the surface in Devon which have been identified as tropical with **lateritic** and **kaolinitic** characteristics (Isaac 1981, 1983). They are thought to be

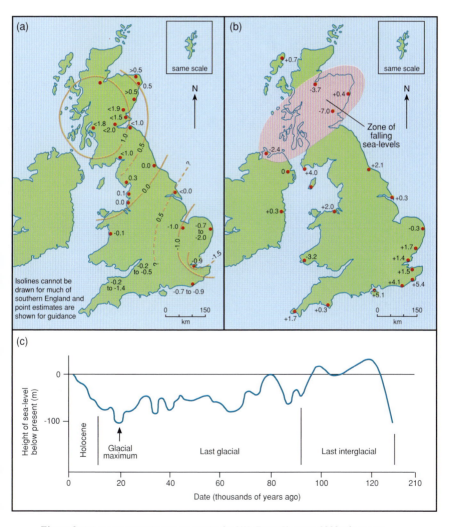

Figure 3: *(a) recent tectonic movements in the UK. From Shennan 1989; (b) recent sea-level changes in the UK. From Carter 1989; (c) sea-level changes over the last glacial-interglacial cycle. From Brunsden and Goudie 1981.*

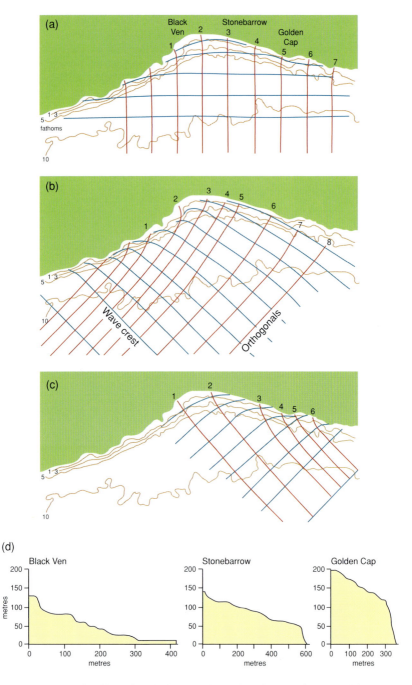

Figure 4: The effects of sea-bed topography on the refraction of waves and the effect of wave energy on cliff form. (a) wind south-west, period 5 seconds; (b) wind south, period 5 seconds; (c) wind south-east, period 5 seconds (d) typical cliff shapes from west to east. After Langridge, 1980.

of Early Tertiary age. Very similar reddish stony soils are found on the top of Stonebarrow Hill and Black Ven and are exposed on the clifftops. In general, therefore, the deposits and the flat hilltops can be considered as remarkably stable features which have been developing for the last 60 million years.

These ancient soils have also suffered from the effects of the extreme climatic changes of the Pleistocene Ice Age. The most effective of these were the cold phases associated with the glaciations. West Dorset had a **periglacial** climate and the plateau soils were churned by frost. The flint gravels were broken into smaller angular fragments and oriented parallel to the hillslopes as they moved downhill by **solifluction** processes. The hillslopes are now mantled by very thick '**head**' deposits produced at this time. Beautiful deposits of this kind can be seen in the coastal sections exposed on the top of Golden Cap and give some indication of the form of the Ice Age cliffs which degraded behind the exposed sea floor. The slopes are also affected by massive landslides which seem to have occurred during the wetter and colder conditions. All along the flanks of the inland slopes of Timber Hill, Stonebarrow and Golden Cap are remnants of these ancient slides. Even much of Charmouth (see Photo 2) stands on such a feature and the top of the sea cliffs at Westhay contains old rotational landslides submerged in a sea of old **scree** and solifluction waste.

Erosional energy

The last control of landform evolution is the erosional energy of the shore. The OS maps (1:50 000 sheets 193 and 194) of the west Dorset coast show that it is characterised by a sequence of shallow asymmetrical bays which flatten eastwards from headlands – for example, the bays running from Lyme Regis (SY 340920), Golden Cap (SY 405922) and Thorncombe Beacon (SY 436915).

It is also a common feature that the nearshore depth of water increases eastwards along the bay away from the headlands. The most common direction from which the wind arrives on these shores is from the west, south-west and south, with a characteristic wave period of 3-6 seconds and a wave height of 1-5m. In one exceptional storm in 1979, waves of an 8-second period and 14m height were experienced. Other typical storm directions are north-west and south-east. The waves are bent (refracted) as they approach the irregular shoreline. Relatively more wave energy is dispersed in the shallower water near the headland end of the bays compared to that which arrives, after less interference, on the deeper and straighter stretches. This means that there is more erosional energy towards the east and the cliffs here are less protected from sea or wave erosion (see Figure 4).

This variation in wave energy is particularly responsible for the extent, form and steepness of the three cliffs: Black Ven (SY 355932), Stonebarrow (SY 375928) and Golden Cap (Figure 4d). Black Ven is a deep embayment with pronounced benches and large mud lobes which project into the sea. It is at the low-energy western end of the bay. Stonebarrow is in an intermediate position with two prominent benches and a 40-50m high coastal cliff. Golden Cap (191m) is the highest cliff on the south coast of England and has a much steeper profile. It is at the high-energy end of the bay, and while it does have active mudslides, these do not manage to survive long on the foreshore once rapid cliff failure has ceased.

Access and orientation

The best general view of the west Dorset coast is from the Cobb at Lyme Regis. This can be coupled with a short walk along Monmouth Beach and the Esplanade, including the site of Cliff House, Langmoor and Lister Gardens to view the current instability and the new coastal protection measures.

COASTAL ZONE PROCESSES 1

The landslides of west Dorset

The conditions described above determine the main processes which operate along the Dorset coast.

Mass movement is a general term used by geomorphologists to describe all the forms of slope failure mentioned previously. The most common forms of mass movements on the Dorset cliffs are rock falls, rotational landslides and slumps, mudslides, and mudflows and sand runs (see Figure 5).

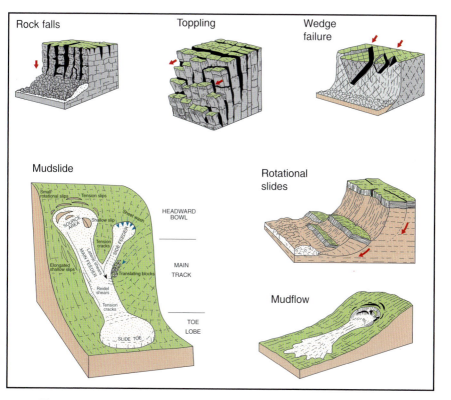

Figure 5: Some common forms of mass movement on the Dorset coast.
From: Allison 1992, after Brunsden and Goudie 1981.

Rock falls

These occur on the steep cliffs and involve the detachment of loose blocks of consolidated or competent rock and enormous slabs which are defined by joints and faults. They collapse and fall onto the debris slopes or beaches below. In addition, beneath Stonebarrow and Golden Cap whole sections of the cliff face sometimes settle like a strong person buckling at the knees and bulge out on to the beach, or alternatively topple over like a pile of children's bricks. Golden Cap often displays pronounced pinnacles. These are dangerous and dawdling is not recommended.

Rotational landslides and slumps

The steep slopes at the tops and in the middles of the cliffs are often the scars of landslides which have settled down the cliff along a curved basal surface so that the mass, which remains intact, rotates or tilts backwards, inland, to leave a depression between the scar and the landslide. This may be later filled by a pond or by fine debris. The toe of the landslide commonly bulges forward. These may occur singly or as a series (known as multiple rotational landslides) so that a 'staircase' of tilted benches occurs downslope. Where landslides are very small they are often termed slumps.

Mudslides

These are masses of softened clay or sandy debris which move forward across the structural benches by sliding. Their form is very similar to that of a miniature glacier in that they have a bowl-shaped head, which is the source of their material, an elongate track through which the material moves, and a pronounced lobe where they come to rest. Where a mudslide has newly occurred it is often possible to see a shiny, slippery and sometimes scratched or striated surface across which movement has occurred. This is called a shear surface (see Figure 5), which means that the rock has been split by shearing forces to allow movement (lateral shears and Reidel shears). This failure line comes to the surface at the edge of the mudslide and is often just like the effect of a knife cut through a mass of plasticine. Mudslides on the Dorset coast sometimes occur as cascades so that the mud which falls over the edge of one bench falls on to the back of the mudslide below. This is called loading and is a major reason why a lower mudslide moves, in order to relieve the forces generated by the mud which has fallen on its back. The front of a mudslide on the beach is often pushed upwards by the forces involved to form a toe ridge which bulges out of the shingle. The cracks on the mudslide surface are analogous to the crevasses observed on glaciers. The general mass or matrix of the mudslide is distinctive, with blocks of unweathered and disturbed clay, and can be easily observed where the toes have been trimmed by the sea.

Mudflows and sand runs

When the slope-forming materials are saturated with water and suddenly collapse, the concentration of sediment may be low enough and the water pressures high enough to allow the clays and sands to flow across the surface. Sometimes only streams of muddy water are observed, but more often very liquid clay lobes and runs of sand spread out as low-angle slopes with pressure ridges and flow structures rather similar to the features seen in a spilt bowl of porridge.

Example 1: Higher Sea Lane

Before describing the geomorphology of Black Ven it is worth examining a small mudslide, the Higher Sea Lane mudslide (SY 363930). This is suggested so that the important features of a mudslide can be studied in the context of a relatively simple mudslide before advancing to the complex area of Black Ven.

The Higher Sea Lane mudslide is 150m long and 50m wide, and lies between the cafe on the sea front at Charmouth and Black Ven itself (Figure 6), descending from the low cliffs approximately 200m west from the Charmouth car park. It starts from a steep upper slope which has been actively eroding towards Higher Sea Lane, Charmouth. The

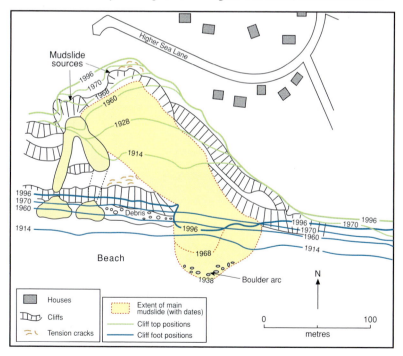

Figure 6: The mudslide at Higher Sea Lane, Charmouth.
This mudslide consists of two main sources or 'bowls' and several separate mudflow tracks. From Denness et al. 1975.

track is complex, but on the eastern side the shear surface is clearly visible, whilst towards the west the mudslide is more diffuse with a multitude of tension cracks. Towards the sea the mud moves over a second steep lower slope which is an eroded embayment in the sea cliff. The slide then forms a lobe on to the beach which is in two portions. On the east, a triangle of firmer grass-covered ground represents the remains of an earlier slide. In the centre, with clear boundaries, is the most recent failure that occurred during the 1960s. The source area retreated at rates of 1-5m per year, the pattern of which is shown in Figure 6. The earliest recorded movement occurred in the 1920s and a failure in 1938 formed a mudslide which spread far out onto the beach, the lobate margin of which is now preserved in the sands by arcs of boulders (visible only at low tide). The toe was then eroded until on 13 May 1968 a second lobe slid out of the middle of the 1938 failure. This lobe has also now been eroded back to the line of the adjacent sea cliffs. The lobe moved again in 1986-87. A careful examination of this slide will reveal the nature of the debris accumulation processes, shear surfaces, surface cracking, and mudslide composition. The adjacent sea cliffs to the east and west have been retreating more slowly (0.5m per year – 25-40m since 1914) as shown by successive OS maps.

It is clear that this mudslide has been threatening the houses on Higher Sea Lane for a long period. Fortunately, however, the danger has been recognised and remedial drainage measures to lower the water pressures in the hill have been taken to slow up and possibly stop coastal cliff recession.

A comprehensive report of this slide has been published by Denness *et al.* (1975) who drew attention to the fact that a contributory cause was the intersection, by the retreating cliff, of late-glacial mudflow deposits. Recent studies now show that a very large area of Charmouth has been built on ancient slides and some houses do show minor structural damage. Fortunately, as at Higher Sea Lane, the problem seems to be solved by adequate drainage.

Access

The seaward car park at Charmouth (SY 364931) is the best starting point for visits to the Higher Sea Lane mudslide and Black Ven. To view the relationship of the mudslide to the Higher Sea Lane houses, one should walk westwards along the footpath on the clifftop, then down the mudslide to the beach. Alternatively, the toe of the slide can be easily reached along the shore.

Continue along the shore to reach the coarse boulders which mark the eroded toe of the 1958 mudslide of Black Ven. It is advisable to follow clearly marked paths close to the edge of the sea during any winter visit, but in dry periods it is possible to walk up the axis of the mudslide to view the features of the track and source. Between the eastward and westward mudslides there is a narrow eroded ridge which can be ascended with care, keeping to the westward side, and with a little scrambling through vegetation one can reach a high point overlooking the most active mudslide. **This mudslide can be deep and dangerous and should not be crossed except very close to the sea.** On returning, it is useful to walk straight down to the sea to view the structures and matrix of the slide revealed by coastal erosion.

Example 2: Black Ven

Black Ven (Figure 7 and Photos 1 and 2), the most active complex of mudslides in the British Isles and one of the largest in Europe, has suffered three major phases of instability in the twentieth century. It consists of rotational landslides and slumps on the Upper Greensand rocks at the top of the slope; mudslides, mudflows and sandflows on the benches; and rockfalls from the steep slopes. The area is very boggy and the name 'Ven' is probably derived from the word 'fen' (or bog). Black Ven is approximately 130m high and the cliff profile shows several strongly developed benches, supported by Belemnite Stone and other resistant horizons elsewhere in the Lower Lias. The uppermost cliffs collapse in single and multiple rotational landslides to form a thick debris slope which receives the water that seeps out of the permeable Chert beds and Foxmould (Upper Greensand). When saturated, this material moves across the upper

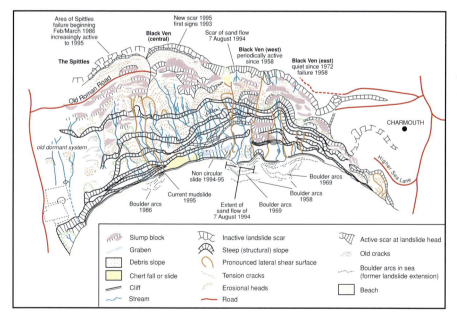

Figure 7: The Black Ven landslide complex.
This complex consists of two main sources on bowls with long tracks descending over steep cliffs and benches to form high lobes across the beach. The former extent of the slides is now revealed by the boulders which extend into the sea. Source: Brunsden 1969, Denness et al. 1975, Conway 1974. Reproduced in part by permission of the Director, Institute of Geological Sciences. Crown Copyright reserved. Additional data by the authors.

21

(a)

(b)

(c)

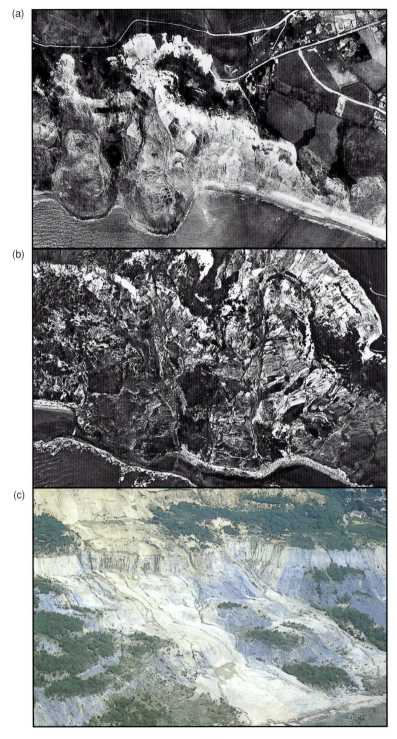

Photo 1 (opposite): Aerial images of Black Ven showing how the cliffs have changed between (a) 1958 and (b) 1969 and (c) 1988. In (c) the failure from the Spittles in February 1986 emphasises the dynamic nature of the area. Between the Spittles and Black Ven (west) the degraded scar of a mudslide of unknown age is visible.
Photos: (a) Hunting Surveys Ltd, (b) Fairey Surveys for D Brunsden and (c) Jim Chandler.

bench and falls 20m on to the next bench. This mud, supplemented by material from the Liassic cliffs, is then funnelled into mudslide tracks which change their courses according to the activity of the complex (Photo 2). When very active, intermixing streams of mud pour continuously over the terraces to merge into broad lobes which push steadily out into the sea. When activity ceases or slows up, the toes are then eroded back by the sea to leave behind arcuate areas of boulders on the foreshore. This process is repeated through time so that the resulting depositional areas are a complex of slides, flows, gullies, pressure ridges, tension cracks, and even domes of clay heaved up by water pressures within the moving mass. The area becomes vegetated during inactive or quiet periods, the maturity of the plant communities reflecting the relative age of each part of the lobes.

Movements of Black Ven have attracted scientific attention for nearly a century, the burning cliff photographs of 1908 and the loss of the Charmouth-Lyme Regis coast road in the 1920s being notable early events. Since then there has been intermittent failure almost every year and two periods of pronounced activity: late summer 1957 to 9-10 February 1958, when the mudslides extended nearly 100m

Photo 2: Mudslides at Black Ven, March 1990. Photo: Andrew Goudie.

across the beach; and 1969 to approximately 1973, when the westernmost flow track showed great erosional activity. Both events are well recorded by aerial photographs which demonstrate the rapidity with which erosion along such coasts can take place (Photos 2a, b and c). Cliff retreat of 5-30m per year is characteristic of the active periods, while between major events the coastal erosion of the toe has been between 15m and 40m per year.

An eyewitness to the 1958 event wrote:

'I saw a great mass of Upper Greensand densely covered with bushes and trees slowly crawling downwards from the highest terrace, while below a river of liquid mud was slipping over the low cliff above the beach ... the main movement in the night must have been very rapid, as by daylight a huge fan of debris, crested with uprooted trees, had pushed out across the beach to beyond low water neap tides.'

This description vividly illustrates both the dynamic and the dangerous nature of this site.

Black Ven was also the subject of research activity during the 1980s and 1990s. This included instrumentation of the precipitation, soil properties, pore water pressures, and surface and subsurface movement. These show that the patterns are very complex with a

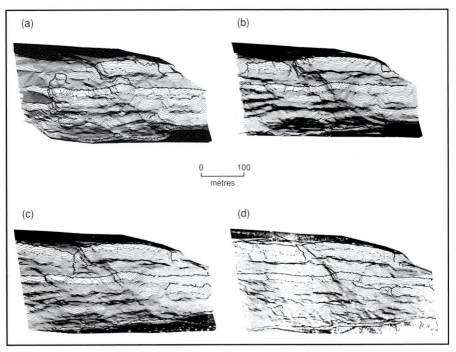

Figure 8: Isometric views of the Black Ven system in (a) 1958; (b) 1969; (c) 1976; (d) 1988.
This shows how the system can give a clear visual 3D image of landscape change.
Source: Chandler and Brunsden 1995.

wide range of conditions needed for renewal of movement as the seasons progress.

Perhaps the most exciting advances, however, have been made by the application of advanced aerial photograph measurement techniques and their use to produce digital erosion maps. The total landform change for 1946-88 is summarised digitally in Figure 8. For the first time we have a picture of the behaviour, in time, of an entire landslide complex. This has been achieved for the time periods (a) 1946-58, (b) 1959-69, (c) 1970-76 and (d) 1977-88. The study shows that up until 1956 there had been a progressive steepening of the cliffs by marine erosion. Sudden failures, fast enough to trap a person on the beach, took place in the winter of 1958. Following this initial rapid movement the cliffs adjusted. Lobes of mud were built up in the sea and, over the next ten years, the surge of erosion moved back to displace the upper cliff by as much as 90m, producing a staircase of benches and steep cliffs (Figure 9). The main processes were the cascades of material over the terrace edges, the parallel retreat of the undercliffs and the rapid transport of material away from the foot of the cliffs and across the benches by mudslides.

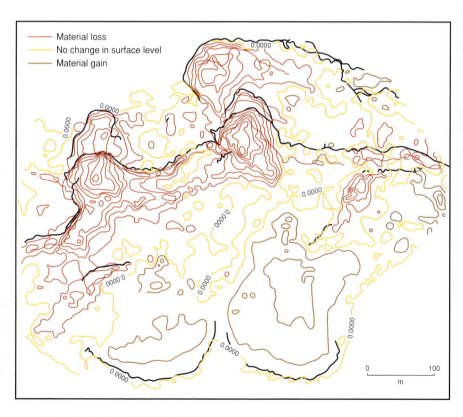

Figure 9: Erosion of Black Ven 1958-69 from analytical photogrammetry.
Source: Chandler and Brunsden 1995.

Finally, the mud enters the sea and beach systems. This is the first documented example of a slope retreating rapidly but episodically in time and space but maintaining an unchanging slope form. The remarkable interdependence between process and form is demonstrated by the sheer scale of the movements involved. Between 1958 and 1988 over 200 000m³ of sediment was transported from the cliff to the sea over the staircase of terraces. The striking fact is that except for initial adjustments the average form did not change, which can only mean that the input from the cliffs was transported to the sea in such a manner that input equals output over a 50+ year period. This is probably the only documented case of a slope system maintaining a steady state of processes and characteristic form.

Access

The new Spittles landslide is best seen by leaving the A3052 road on the Old Lyme Road at SY 344927 and taking the footpath through the fields. Follow the paths through the rough ground and vegetation to the viewpoint overlooking Black Ven (SY 351930).

Example 3: Stonebarrow

Stonebarrow Hill (SY 375928) is a broad ridge aligned north-east to south-west whose inland slopes, which are mantled with a rubbly debris, known as head, and degraded landslides, descend to the River Char on the west and to a small stream known as Westhay Water on the east. The seaward end of the ridge is truncated by marine erosion to form a 40-50m high coastal cliff, overlooked by a large amphitheatre, usually called Fairy Dell (Photo 3), which is 1400m west to east, a maximum of 350m north to south and 85m high.

The rocks consist of Chert, Upper Greensand and Gault of Cretaceous age unconformably resting on Middle and Lower Liassic strata. The slope complex contains three nearly subparallel cliff-lines separated by landslides and debris-covered benches (Photo 4), which occur at the base of the Cretaceous and at the outcrop of the Green Ammonite Beds in the Lias (see Table 1 on page 9 and Figure 10). The uppermost cliff is a steep (50-70°) arcuate landslide scar up to 40m high, developed in the Chert and Upper Greensand (Foxmould). The lower part of the scar is a scree slope at 35° and at a lower level are multiple rotational landslide blocks. The first of these, which bears the broken remnants of a radar station (Photo 5), slipped at 8.00a.m. on 14 May 1942, when approximately 28m of the cliff subsided, displacing a surface area of 7500m², and at the same time a grove of mature beech trees, known as Cain's Folly, also settled down the cliff. The slope of the building gives an immediate indication of the amount of tilt suffered by a landslide as it rotates on its curved failure surface.

The seaward landslides occurred at some time prior to the OS map of 1887, when it is thought that an area of 25 000-30 000m² of land

Photo 3: Vertical aerial image of Stonebarrow Hill, 1969.
The arcuate scar, the displaced block of Upper Greensand and the mudslide hollows and gullies on the Liassic rocks which also form the sea cliff can all be seen clearly. Photo: Fairey Surveys Ltd for D Brunsden.

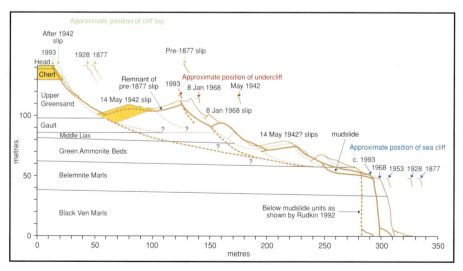

Figure 10: Section through Stonebarrow Hill.
The dotted line represents the approximate changes (to 1993) since the original was drawn in 1968. Note that on either side of the section of the sea cliff, retreat has been much faster below mudslide embankments. Source: Brunsden and Jones 1976.

Photo 4: Stonebarrow Hill, looking towards Charmouth. Photo: Andrew Goudie.

Photo 5: The foundered radar building at Stonebarrow. Photo: Andrew Goudie.

was involved. Between these failures, and since 1942, the scars and blocks have slowly degraded and the clifftop has retreated by approximately 17m (0.53m per year) through small-scale failure. For example, a debris slide 5m x 30m x 1m occurred on the back scar on 8 January 1968. Two more occurred in February 1993. The present rate of retreat, measured by survey marks inserted in the face, is 0.15m per year. Erosion is thus clearly spasmodic or episodic in nature and the landscape itself is dominated by features caused by large-scale landslides rather than small-scale events. The scree slope has been formed since 1942 and gives a good indication of the rate of slope development on soft coastal materials.

In the middle of Fairy Dell there is an 'undercliff' and a lower platform which consists mainly of Middle and Lower Lias rocks. The cliff is steep (30-45°) but fairly free of debris, for material is being continuously removed from the slope base by large multiple rotational landslides, mudslides, mudflows, creep and gully erosion. When the mudslides are active the rates of movement can be as high as 90m per year, while the rotational slips move seawards at rates of up to 20m per year. The 'undercliff' is being eroded at approximately 0.5-2.6m per year. Some parts have retreated 33-60m between 1946 and 1969. Thick vegetation renders these mudslides on the lower slopes very inaccessible.

The mudslide material, which is usually 1-2m deep, moves seasonally towards the sea cliff where it either breaks off in pieces and falls to the beach or slides into one of the many gullies that give a crenellated edge to the clifftop (Photo 4). The rotational landslides on the lower bench also fall on to the beach, but tend to be more episodic in occurrence than the cyclic or seasonal mudslides. The failures of 1942 were accompanied by at least four large rotational slides on the lower bench which are still partly visible in the landscape. They do, however, break up into smaller units as these move towards the sea – a process known as block disruption.

The sea cliffs retreat at 0.4-0.5m per year, a total of 35m from 1887 to 1969. Retreat is achieved through rockfalls and large-scale collapse, the debris becoming incorporated in an accumulation at the foot of the cliffs.

The landslide complex seems to evolve in the following way. Sea or wave erosion removes debris from the store of sediment at the foot of the cliffs and progressively cuts into the cliff itself. This increases the rate of debris transport from the lower bench above the cliffs by undermining the toes of the mudslides above and creating new failures in the 'undercliff'. This in turn brings down material from the toe of the pre-1887 slides above, which causes them to move seawards. Thus a wave of erosional aggression reaches the Upper Greensand cliff and once again failure occurs and more farmland is lost.

The sea cliffs lose material throughout the year but peak activity occurs in winter. The individual quantities involved are small but the frequencies are high. The retreat of the sea cliff is transferred into a seasonal behaviour in the mudslides above with maximum activity in winter (January-March) and in wet years. The mudslides attack the undercliff causing new slope failures approximately every 40 years; for example, the last remnants of the undercliff failures of 1942 were actually destroyed in 1982-84. New failures take place from the toes of the rotational failures on the upper tier. These begin to settle and small failures take place on the scar as it too prepares to fail again. Currently, small failures are beginning on the scar 50 years after the last movements. When the scar will collapse again is unknown, although the historical evidence suggests c.100+ years between movements.

Access

Stonebarrow Hill can be reached in two ways: from Charmouth car park across the footbridge over the River Char and by following the footpath close to the cliff edge to the crest of the hill. If travelling in minibuses or cars, return through the town towards Bridport and immediately after crossing the Char take a small lane past Newlands (SY 371935) to the National Trust car park at the top of the hill. If it is felt necessary to descend a little way towards the radio-location station this can be achieved down a very steep rocky path immediately to the east of the destroyed buildings.

GOLDEN CAP ESTATE COAST WALKS

Photo 6: The coastline from Black Ven (foreground) to Stonebarrow (middleground) and Golden Cap (background). *Photo: Andrew Goudie.*

The coastline between Stonebarrow and Golden Cap is marked by a succession of small but interesting landslides. At Westhay Cliff (SY 394926) shallow slumps and mudslides are cutting back into the remnants of rotational slides and scree material which have descended all the way (c.100m) from the top of Stonebarrow. The stratigraphic order of the top of the hill, namely two Chert bands and the Upper Greensand, is preserved, though tilted at a steep angle. Such relict landslides mantle all of the inland slopes at this point and even cause an inversion of relief at Ridge Cliff, because the displaced cherts on the ridge are more resistant than the rocks on either side.

At Ridge Cliff and Broom Cliff there are beautiful bowl shaped mudslide heads and, near Seatown just east of St Gabriel's Water, the control of landslide form by bedding becomes evident with the development of a **graben** over 100m long. This provides a perfect small teaching example of a non-circular failure.

Golden Cap is a spectacular viewpoint from which scenes toward Lyme Regis and Portland Bill can be described. Unlike Black Ven and Stonebarrow, it is a true headland, with a mass movement complex on either side, meeting at a very steep and unstable cliff point known as Wear Cliffs. The yellow slopes above are called Shorne Cliff. To the west lies Kitwells Cliff (SY 400921) which is an interesting shallow embayment containing two lines of active rotational slumps of cylindrical or 'slice' form, separated by ponds and washed debris. The sea cliffs beneath are very unstable and often swept clear by waves. Still on the west, and immediately under the line of gorse on the crest of Golden Cap, is an impressive mudslide. This occurred in 1962 but is so active that despite the rapid marine erosion at its base it is still able to push a high lobe of mud into the sea and now effectively prevents shingle from passing around the coast to Seatown beach. This sort of activity must have occurred many times before because as one moves around the headland several areas of boulders on the foreshore mark the lines of former mudslide lobes. Towards the east, however, the mudslide heads are now relatively stable and the tracks have been incised by gully erosion into a V-shape form. Small active landslides form a shallow cliff-line towards Seatown.

The form of the cliff is different from those previously described, mainly because of the active wave erosion at the base of the cliffs (discussed on pages 17-19) but also because the geological succession now includes a thick sequence of sands from the Upper and Middle Lias.

The flanks of Golden Cap are also interesting because they are covered with the remains of shallow slips and solifluction deposits. Good sections are seen on the ascent to Golden Cap and a fine impression of the form of the late-glacial slopes can be gained from the sections on the eastern side of Shorne Cliff.

The descent to Seatown is also of increasing interest. During the gales of 1987, 1989, 1995 and 1996 several metres were taken from the foot of the western cliffs and the aggressive wave of erosion is now eating back to reactivate old slides. The beach itself has suffered severely. For several months the beach was distributed to the eastern end and a bare fossiliferous clay platform extended one-third of the way along the beach. In 1996 the position was reversed and a deeply incised clay platform was exposed on the eastern side. Very severe erosion took place at this time. This general story of beach lowering and consequent erosion of the cliffs continues all the way to West Bay (Photo 7). New failures can be seen at the centre of Ridge Cliff, on the eastern side of Doghouse Hill and below Thorncombe Beacon. Eype Mouth is renowned for the speed of coastal erosion and beach lowering whilst Fault Corner, immediately below the caravan site on West Cliff, has had postcards made of its landslide since 1908. The last major movement took place when the waste from the regrading of

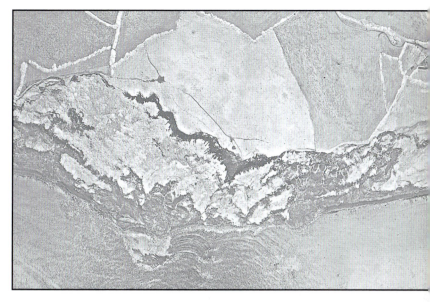

Photo 7: Vertical aerial photograph of Golden Cap, 1969.
Wear Cliffs is marked by the patch of bare ground on the clifftop. The arcs of the boulders in the sea mark the front edge of former large mudslides of unknown date. Wave refraction can be seen on a small scale as the waves approach the small bays beneath the complex cliffs. One-third of the distance from the bottom is the 1962 mudslide which closed off littoral drift. The build-up of beach gravel to the west (bottom) and the depletion under Golden Cap is obvious. Photo: Fairey Surveys for D Brunsden.

the cliff and the extension of the promenade at West Bay was placed in the convenient hollow of the old slide and the whole slip suddenly moved into the sea! This cliff is made of Fuller's Earth, one of the most unstable clays known to science. Difficulties in handling these materials can be seen in the state of the remedial measures, the cracking of the sea-wall and the rapid recession of the cliff where the protection measures cease. During the last four years erosion has worsened and the houses at the top of the cliff were threatened by failure. During 1995-96 major engineering works have remade the cut slope with over 40,000 tonnes of rip-rap and extensive drainage.

The last cliffs to be affected are East Cliff and Burton Cliff. Both are composed of Bridport Sands with a very thin capping of Inferior Oolitic Limestones and Lower Fuller's Earth clay. The rocks are a rhythmic alternation of hard, carbonate cemented, burrowed sands with less well cemented and burrowed sands which weather at different rates to give a remarkable ridged form. The joint patterns are also picked out to allow the formation of buttresses and recesses (Photo 8). The cliffs suffer rapid undercutting when the beach is low. A perfect wave-cut notch develops and the buttresses become unsupported. When the stress is great enough a buttress will fall to give temporary protection at the slope foot. The history of this can largely be read in the cliff form, because a very smooth portion of the cliff is left behind which has to weather again to yield the typical ledges.

The top of East Cliff is also one of the few places in coastal Britain where it is possible to observe (from below only!) sections in **cambered** slopes. The general unloading of the slopes, toward the rivers, has opened up the main joints which have then been infilled with the debris from the rocks above. The age of this is unknown but may well relate to the low sea-levels of the last glaciation when the buried channels of the Brit and Bredy rivers were formed.

Photo 8: East Cliff near West Bay. *Note the cambering joints opening in the centre of the photo at the top of the cliff. Photo: Sillson Communications, Wareham.*

Access

Golden Cap can be reached by walking from a National Trust car park (SY 412934) just off the Morecombelake-Chideock road on a turning known as Muddy Ford Lane. The footpath runs around Langdon Hill and is signposted by the National Trust. Alternatively walk along the cliffs from Seatown (SY 420917), or from Stonebarrow Hill. Please respect the country code within all these areas. Perhaps it ought to be emphasised yet again that these cliffs are dangerous, the edges frequently collapse and the dense vegetation often hides deep cracks and deep, wet mud. Full safety precautions should be taken.

COASTAL ZONE PROCESSES 2

Sediment transport and beaches

The second set of processes is that which operates on the beach, nearshore and offshore. It is helpful to consider the beach as a simple system within which sediment transfer takes place. New materials appear on the beach from offshore stores, around headlands, from rivers, dunes or eroding cliffs. They are redistributed along the shore, unless stopped by barriers, by the waves and tidal currents. Some of the material moves to temporary stores in the nearshore and some is permanently lost to the system around headlands or offshore. A dominant or resultant movement in one direction is called longshore drift or loss to a sediment sink (Figure 11). This characterisation of a beach helps us to think of the processes in terms of budgets, movements, fluxes, inputs, outputs, gains, losses and volumes. It also supplies the basis for numerical modelling, and sensible management decisions.

Cliff retreat

The Lyme Regis-Chesil Beach systems are well documented and demonstrate how closely linked the various components of coastal erosion are. Since 1901, the sea cliffs have retreated 0.4-0.7m per year between Black Ven and Stonebarrow. These rates vary from 0-5m per year, with local extreme rates in the storms of 1987 and 1989. Over a long period, the sea cliffs and the tops of the landslide systems retreat at similar rates. This means that there is a steady supply of clay, fine sand, Chert, flint and limestone to the beach at Charmouth and that the cliff form tends to remain the same.

The rates have been calculated by Brunsden 1969, 1973, 1974, and Brunsden and Jones 1976, 1980, and arranged into a coherent story by Bray 1992 (Figure 12). The total volume supplied to the beaches between 1901 and 1988 was over 26 million m^3 or nearly 42 million tonnes. Unfortunately, only a very small proportion of this is capable of forming beach shingle and most of the clay was washed offshore. Only 0.5 million m^3 formed durable material. Much of the sand also went offshore to form the fine deposits of Lyme Bay. It is not known how much material comes onshore from relict stores of gravel. It is believed, however, that most of the available gravel would have been brought in long ago as the post-glacial sea-level rose to its present position. This is confirmed by the offshore sediment maps which show mainly thin deposits of fine materials with some buried gravel

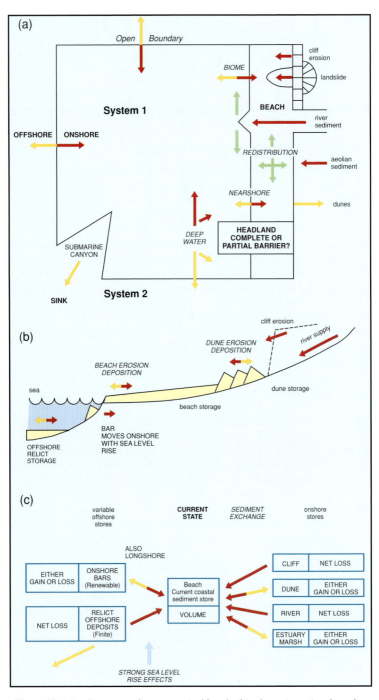

Figure 11: *(a) sediment transfers on a typical beach, (b) schematic section through a beach, (c) the beach exchange model, showing the importance of the finite offshore relict stores.*

offshore from the eastern end of Chesil Beach. It is also thought that there is little material supply around the headlands. The cliffs of the Landslide Nature Reserve at Lyme have deep water offshore. In addition the system has now been closed by the construction of the Cobb which holds all the limestone pebbles at Monmouth Beach (Photo 9). The West Bay beaches have also been short-circuited by harbour mouth piers, so the return exchange of material with Chesil Beach is now very small. As a result the beaches of west Dorset should be regarded as being in a finite and fragile state. They are maintained only by the erosion of their cliffs.

It is also important to recognise that the supply of material is pulsed, not constant. Coastal landslide systems operate episodically and there are long periods during which no sediment is supplied. At these times the beach will become depleted and erosion of the cliff will become easier. The rate will increase, the cliff will steepen and a further failure will bring a flush of gravel to the beach. This will in turn slow down the erosion and the pattern repeats itself.

Similar effects are caused by sequences of wet and dry years which control landslide rates. On the beach, big barriers of mud may build-up and prevent movement from one beach to another along the shore. For example, at Black Ven the beach was completely closed by lobes of mud in 1958 and 1969 and was not reconstituted until the storms of the late 1980s. It has now been closed again by a movement in 1994. Between 1939 and 1949 at Golden Cap, shingle extended continuously along the shore from Charmouth to Seatown and perhaps beyond. Intermittent slides after that time held up material until in 1962 a major mudslide closed the beach just to the west of Golden Cap. No material now moves around the Cap. At Thorncombe Beacon rock debris has created similar sediment transport problems for Eype Beach.

The direction of sediment movement

The net movement along the shore is to the east, under the influence of the south-westerly waves, with only occasional returns during the violent but short-lived easterlies. In the 1980s, for example, there was a net *westward* drift. Various figures are available for the volumes moving along the coast, but the consensus seems to be that in the long term there is a net *eastward* drift of gravel of approximately 2825m^3 per year at Charmouth (4710m^3 including fines) and 3447m^3 per year at St Gabriel's Mouth. Allowing for attrition and losses offshore, this means that c. 2000-2500m^2 per year which used to move alongshore to Seatown, then Eype and Chesil, are accumulating at Golden Cap. The beach increases in both height, volume, coarse grain size and pebble sphericity toward the east. This also means that the Seatown beach is in a very fragile state since it is no longer receiving material. Indeed, over the last few years there have been long periods when the beach was totally lost at the western end with a dramatic exposure of the clay shore platform. In 1996 this was reversed when easterly

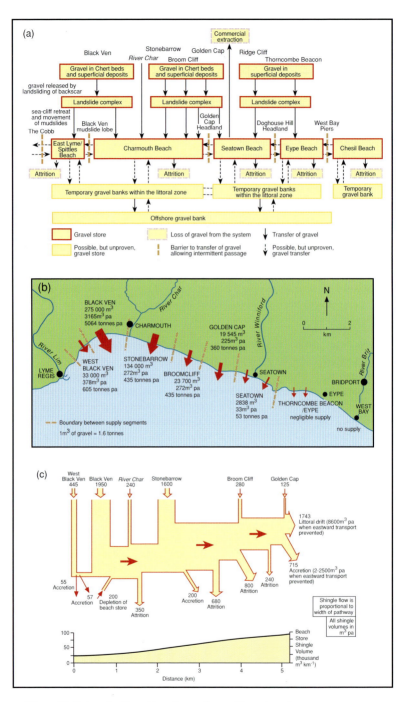

Figure 12: Rates of sediment transfer on the west Dorset coast.
(a) model of the gravel supply from coastal landsliding, (b) coastal erosion gravel supply, 1901-88, (c) gravel flow through Charmouth Beach. Source: Bray 1992.

Photo 9: The Lyme Regis coast.
The closure of the Cobb has had a dramatic effect on littoral drift, as have the groynes further east. Note the erosion and depleted beaches beyond. Photo: Aerofilms Ltd.

winds caused the shingle to drift to the western end and expose the eastern platform. Since 1987 the base of the cliff at this point has been eroding at well over 1m a year and in both 1987 and 1989 over 3m was lost in the gales. During the wet winters of 1994 and 1995 the cliffs responded with an increase of landslide activity.

The episodicity of these processes is worth repeating because a casual visitor might not appreciate that the current beach condition at Charmouth is a reflection of the huge amount of material fed to the beach by extreme landslide activity west of Black Ven since 1986. The beach is composed of large, *angular,* blocky gravel and boulders which still have the white weathered patina of the bedrock from which they are derived. However, when the first edition of this book was written in 1981 the beach was low, with rounded shingle and only a small storm beach of cobbles. Historical records show that the previous times when similar conditions existed were in 1932 (after the mudslides of 1908-28) and in 1960-66 after the mudslides of 1958. Another typical feature is the diversion of the River Char to the east by a coarse gravel spit accumulation at storm beach elevations. This condition is also seen to exist in postcards of the 1930s. The Char itself occasionally breaks through the beach in flood to spread a fan of coarse angular material at its mouth. This last happened in 1979.

Understanding of beach systems therefore requires a knowledge of the sequences of events and time lags as well as the rates. In west Dorset the system seems to operate on a 100+ years timescale.

Photo 10: *A jetty was built at West Bay to facilitate entry to the harbour.* (a) in 1860 it has had little effect on the coastline; (b) by 1985 the cliff had to be protected by a sea-wall. Even this has since been severely damaged by a winter storm. Copyright: (b) Hydration Research Ltd.

Human impact on the coastal system

Mention has been made of the effect of human activity on the coastal system. This continues to be very severe in west Dorset. The construction of the harbour jetty, the Cobb, and its joining to the land in 1756, totally interrupted the supply of sediment to the Lyme Regis frontage (Photo 9). In the eighteenth and nineteenth centuries a succession of sea defence works: sea-walls, retaining walls and groynes were constructed and beach feeding was carried out in 1967 and 1992. In 1993 a major reconstruction was under way with a sea-wall completed in 1995. In 1995, however, the front of Langmoor Garden collapsed and a new consultancy is now being carried out.

The situation was not helped by the removal of material for road and building construction. One author reported that 10 000 tonnes of shore platform limestone was sent to Hull in the nineteenth century (Fowles 1991). From 1840 to 1903 the shore platforms lost 20 000 tonnes to quarrying in a year. The quarrying also attacked the cliffs to the east of the town so that, following worries about the stability of the graveyard, Church Cliff had to be protected.

Further along the coast, at Seatown, West Bay, Cogdon Beach and Chesil there was an active gravel working industry which continued for hundreds of years until stopped by public enquiry in 1983. At West Bay, for example, 8000 tonnes a year were removed in the 1970s. The other significant change here was the construction of the harbour in 1740 and the filling in of the jetties in 1822-24. This stopped the free movement of shingle and promoted the depletion of Eype Beach (Photos 10 a and b). Rapid erosion of the cliff and flooding has necessitated the construction of a sea-wall, its subsequent repair and extension, and the placing of groynes and massive rock armour. In recent gales (1994) the beach has lowered on the Chesil side and erosion threatening East Cliff and Burton Bradstock. Beach material is now returned by lorry to maintain East Beach at West Bay. The power of erosion at this point is testified by the abrasion of the armour stone placed to protect the promenade. The original Portland Stone has now been strengthened by harder rock.

Along the entire length of the coast there are similar examples of the knock-on effects of human actions. At Lyme the most famous case was the collapse of Cliff House in 1962. The degradation of Wear Cliffs caused trouble in 1987 when chalets were damaged by shallow movements. The Cobb Road, Langmoor and Lister Gardens and several of the adjoining houses were affected by movements requiring remedial measures at least 20 times this century. At the present time movements are occurring on all of these sites. East of Lyme there has been a similar story. The repair of Church Cliff in the 1920s, the famous Burning Cliff of 1908, the loss of houses and damage to the car park at East Cliff, the complete failure of the Spittles in 1986, the threat to the Lyme golf course, remedial measures at Higher Sea Lane, the loss of the radar station at Stonebarrow, the appalling new groyne and steps at Charmouth, the urgent need to stabilise the cliffs and beach at Seatown to protect the Anchor Inn and three houses, the loss of land and property at Eype and many other examples serve warning

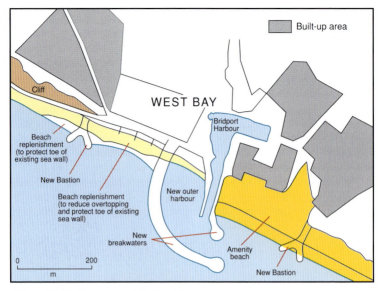

Figure 13: Marina proposals for West Bay.

that the coastal system is indeed to be handled with care. Yet the saga continues – there is now a proposal to build a marina at West Bay (Figure 13).

Here it is worth posing a challenging geomorphological question. Textbooks declare that an apparent build-up of shingle behind the barriers indicates the direction of sediment movement. Figure 13 suggests movement to the west. The historical photographs show that depletion on the *western* side has happened steadily since 1860 (Photo 10). However, all long-term measurements and all other evidence proves that sediment actually moves east under the influence of the westerly, south-westerly dominant winds. It is true that in the 1980s there was a period of easterly winds which built up the beach a little, but in the 1990s there has been a 2m drop in levels and now East Beach is rapidly disappearing. This conundrum has not been recognised in the engineering proposals for the proposed marina and so ...! You might like to make a guess at the cause of this anomaly.

CHESIL BEACH

Photo 11: Chesil Beach and the Fleet. *Photo: Andrew Goudie.*

The sediment pathway continues past West Bay to Chesil Beach (SY 605810), the most impressive shingle ridge in the British Isles (Photo 11). Indeed, Lord Avebury described it as 'probably the most extensive and extraordinary accumulation of shingle in the world'. It is remarkable for its size, its regular crest line, its beautifully even curve, its lack of lateral ridges, and its oft-quoted grading of pebble sizes. As a result, it is the most written about of all landforms in Britain. It is also a dangerous shoreline, hazardous to bathers and ships alike. As Daniel Defoe wrote in 1724:

'Tho' Portland ftands a League off from the main land of Britain, yet it is almost joyn'd by a prodigious Riffe of Beach, that is to fay, of small stone caft up by the sea ... When Ships coming off from the Weftward omit to keep a good offing, or are taken fhort by contrary winds ... if they come to an Anchor, and ride it out, well and good, and if not, they run on shore of that vaft Beach, and are lost without remedy.'

The setting

Chesil Beach (Figure 14) is now considered to begin at Bridport Harbour, West Bay, although before that artificial channel was built, the pebbles obviously continued at least as far as Thorncombe Beacon (SY 435914) and may even have stretched to Golden Cap. The overall length is approximately 29km, of which one-third rests against the mainland. The beach becomes regularly higher and the beach face steeper toward Portland. The height changes from 7m at Abbotsbury to 15m at Chesilton. The width is more variable, 90-120m at Bridport Harbour, 36-60m at Burton, 200-255m at Wyke Regis, and 42-54m at Chesil esplanade. The beach is wider where it is a bank separated from the mainland.

Chesil Beach is composed of between 25 and 100 million tonnes of shingle, which shows a progression in size above low water mark from very fine (pea-sized) at Bridport to 5-7.5cm cobbles at Portland. It is mainly made of flint (from the Chalk), Chert (from the Upper Greensand), limestones (from Portland) and a few 'foreign' rocks: vein quartz, porphyry, black quartzite, and even igneous rocks from the south-west, and quartzites that can be traced to a pebble bed at Budleigh Salterton, Devon. Clearly at some time in the past pebbles were able to move for very long distances around Lyme Bay. The pebbles lie on a finer core beach of sand-pebble matrix and low permeability.

Behind the shingle bank is a tidal lagoon called the Fleet (Photo 11 and Figure 14) which has an area 36-49 km², according to tides, and which varies in width from 50m at the Narrows (SY 650773) to 1000m at Butterstreet Cove (SY 633797). It is very shallow (0.3-3m). Early geomorphologists thought that it was a river valley running parallel to the coast, between the cliffs and Chesil Beach. Today it is believed to be a result of the evolution of Chesil Beach, and came into being as a brackish lagoon enclosed as the Beach developed (Figure 15). It is remarkable that there is no salt marsh development within the Fleet since it is locally quite saline. Recently collected salinity figures show 35%o (parts per thousand) of salt at the entrance, 29.5%o at Shipmoor Point (SY 577836), and 14.8%o at Abbotsbury Swannery (SY 575840). The cliffs behind the Fleet show signs that they were once subjected to direct marine erosion, for in places they

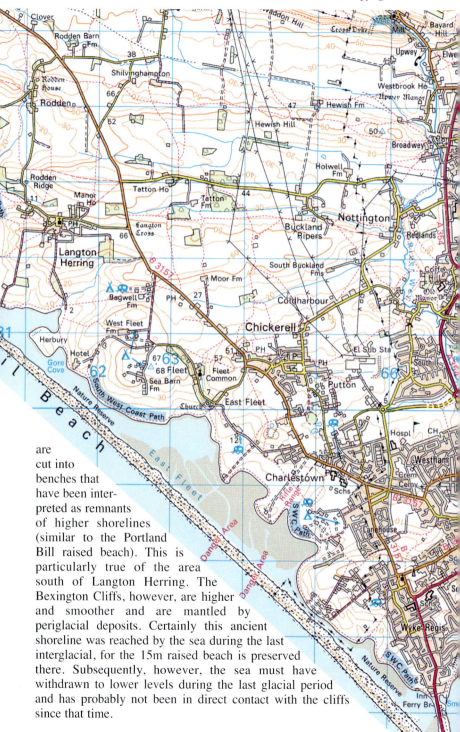

are cut into benches that have been inter-preted as remnants of higher shorelines (similar to the Portland Bill raised beach). This is particularly true of the area south of Langton Herring. The Bexington Cliffs, however, are higher and smoother and are mantled by periglacial deposits. Certainly this ancient shoreline was reached by the sea during the last interglacial, for the 15m raised beach is preserved there. Subsequently, however, the sea must have withdrawn to lower levels during the last glacial period and has probably not been in direct contact with the cliffs since that time.

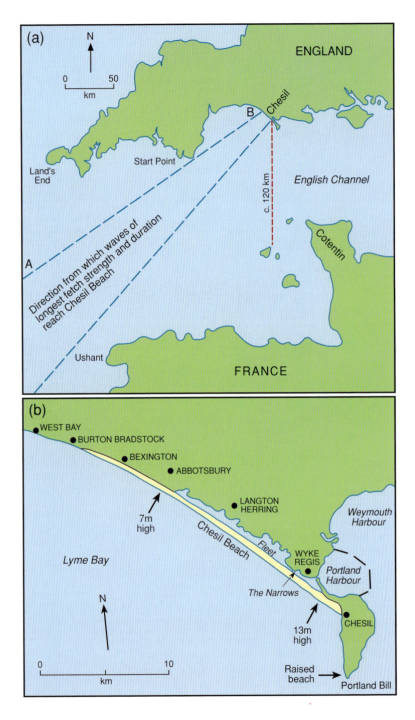

Figure 14: (a) the location of Chesil Beach in relation to possible wave energy, (b) Chesil Beach, the Fleet and the connection to Portland.

Origin

The origin of Chesil Beach, and particularly of the change in pebble sizes, is the subject of a great deal of scientific argument, and no fully acceptable theory has yet been published. An early idea was that the beach was the result of the drift of shingle along the coast (longshore drift) from the south-west, and it grew as a sort of spit which eventually touched the shore at Portland. There is little morphological evidence that this process created the modern beach because there are no lateral ridges or curved spits such as Hurst Castle (Hampshire) or Blakeney Point (Norfolk). The presence of 'foreign' pebbles from such places as Budleigh Salterton does suggest that at some time in the past material did move along the coast, but today any such movement is effectively prevented by the headlands at Lyme Regis, Golden Cap and Thorncombe Beacon. Any movement must have occurred when the beach was further out to sea and not interrupted by headlands. This idea suggests that there was once a major beach offshore.

A third theory is that Chesil Beach was produced by waves which combed up great quantities of material which had been spread across the floor of Lyme Bay by rivers when it was exposed at times of low sea-level (see Figure 15). The material was driven onshore as a beach as sea-levels rose quickly in post-glacial times. One can envisage a bar of shingle moving landward with the rising sea-level (Figure 15) but becoming stranded when no more material was able to be thrown in any substantial amount over a progressively heightened ridge. This suggestion was made because there appeared to be no present suitable source of material (flint and Chert) entering the catchment of the beach from the present day land, and it was therefore believed that the source of the shingle must have been offshore. Recent work on the landslides of west Dorset, however, show that millions of tonnes of flint and Chert debris have fallen (and are still falling) into the sea beyond Thorncombe Beacon. It is only necessary to envisage the beach as being a few tens of metres offshore from its present position for this material to have been directly supplied to the beach. The inclusion of pebbles from Beer and Budleigh Salterton can also be explained in this way. Thus although, as we shall see, the beach has moved onshore, it is useful but not essential to postulate that this has necessarily been from a great distance out to sea.

The evidence that the beach has been driven onshore is that boreholes show that lagoonal clays and peats, which were laid down in a once wider Fleet, extend under the beach towards the seaward face. At the time of publication (1996) great blocks of peat have been eroded from the seaward face and thrown over the beach at Abbotsbury. In addition, of course, it is known that in historical and recent storms pebbles are thrown over the beach crest into the Fleet, across the Weymouth and Portland road, and in 1979 through the houses and windows of Chesilton. Damage to property and flooding often occurs at the Portland end of the beach (Photo 12). Iron-stained pebbles from an older beach surface can be seen to be buried beneath whiter, more recent, material alongside the Naval Helicopter Station (HMS Osprey) at the Portland end. Current measurements of the movement of the beach between the Fleet and Chesilton show that the beach crest, episodically and in storms, is rolling over by as much as 1m per ten years, although there is uneven activity along the beach.

A possible historical sequence or chronology for the evolution of Chesil Beach has been proposed by Alan Carr and colleagues of English Nature, based on many years of meticulous borehole investigations and pollen analysis. The first stage in the evolution of

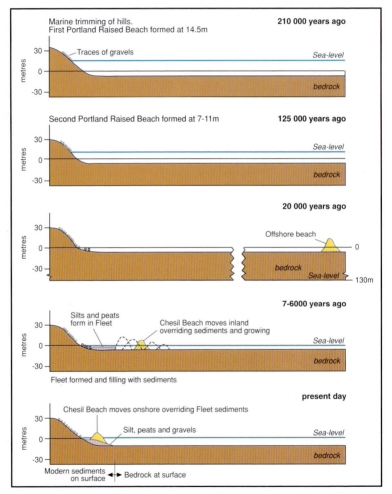

Figure 15: The origin of Chesil Beach.
A bar of shingle formed on the exposed sea floor during a period of low sea-levels and driven onshore by waves as the sea-level rose from the last glaciation towards the present. The final section shows the beach now attached to the land and overriding the peats formed in the once wide Fleet.
After: Carr and Seaward, 1990, 1991.

the area was when the sea trimmed the hills landward of the Fleet to cut raised shorelines. The last of these shorelines and its associated solifluction deposit appears to be of last interglacial (Ipswichian) and last glacial (Devensian) age.

The peat deposits recovered from boreholes suggest that the sea-level was at -45m approximately 10 000 years ago. The sea-level then rose rapidly, averaging 1.5m every 100 years, as the ice caps melted (Figure 16), and Chesil was driven onshore as a bar of material from the river gravels spread across the enlarged coastal plain. Organic silt deposits occur in the boreholes on top of bedrock at Langton Herring and this implies that beginning about 7000 BP very rapid deposition of mud took place in the Fleet, so that by about 4-5000 years ago it had become very shallow, and the beach was established much in its present position. Its subsequent history has been of a slow movement onshore during storm conditions, with cliff erosion now taking place at Burton Bradstock and West Bay and an orientation towards the maximum exposure to wind and waves from the south-west.

If one draws a line from Chesil Beach south-west towards the Atlantic (Figure 14) it will be seen that nothing lies in the path of the winds and the waves until we reach the Americas. Maximum wave energy can therefore reach Chesil Beach and this must be responsible for the perfect development of the beach, its great height in this particular location, and the grading of the shingle. Moreover, the beach is oriented virtually perpendicular to the full majesty of the sea.

Photo 12: Chesil Beach and Portland Harbour seen from the Isle of Portland.
Photo: Andrew Goudie.

The grading of the shingle

Most accounts of Chesil Beach emphasise that there is a remarkably regular grading of the size of shingle and associated change of beach gradient along the shore. Recent studies by Carr and Seaward (1990, 1991) show, however, that the situation is really much more complex. A casual observer visiting successive locations along the beach would be impressed by the increasing size. If careful sampling is carried out across, within and along the beach, it can be shown that the materials on the beach crest and the seaward face are different, with coarser material at the top and finer at the edge of the sea. Below low water mark the pebbles tend to be coarser and variable. Overall the pebbles do get bigger and more similarly sized towards the east, but while they are generally smaller they are also much more variable towards the west. Both large and small sizes are seen between high and low water mark with rapid lateral variations in both space and time. There is finer material deep within the beach, grading down towards present beach level. These variations reflect wave activity prior to any visit, variations in local sources of supply of material, and commercial exploitation of beach material. Up until 1983 as much as 27 000 tonnes of shingle were removed commercially per year, and 1000 tonnes per year of coarse pebbles (commercial pebble picking) were taken from the eastern end. This slightly affected the scientific results from pebble measurement programmes.

Despite this complexity it is still believed by many authors that there is a differential movement of large and small pebbles along the beach. An early idea was that all the pebbles could be transported eastwards along the coast by the south-westerly and westerly waves, but that only smaller grades could be moved backwards to the west by waves of smaller fetch from other directions. Recent measurements also show that once waves are big enough to move the thicker pebbles they will travel more rapidly than smaller ones because they present a bigger surface area to the sea and are less impeded by surface roughness. It is worth noting that any explanation must take into account the sorting which must have taken place when the beach was far offshore and driven to its present position. Explanation must also recognise the complexity of the dynamic wave climate (height, frequency, duration, angle of approach), the sorting which took place as the beach came onshore with rising sea-level, the sediment availability, the transport size threshold and the boundary shear stresses. Continuing research work will no doubt add to our knowledge of these intriguing problems.

The dynamism of Chesil Beach

Chesil Beach is very dynamic. Ordnance surveys from 1846 to 1990 show that there is a tendency for the beach to become lower but to move further inland with time. These trends are very variable

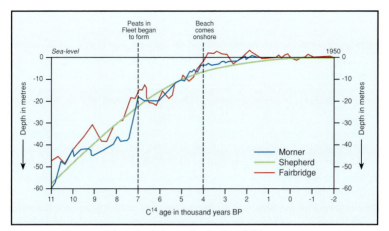

Figure 16: The curve of sea-level change for the last 13 000 years.
This is as suggested by evidence collected by three authors: Morner (1968), Shepard (1963) and Fairbridge (1961). All agree that sea-level has risen from the low levels of the last glaciation toward the present level at a rate of approximately 1.5m per 100 years, slowing down as present levels were reached.

due to sea-level rise, the frequency of storms and changing beach volume. Storms can have a dramatic effect. One event, in 1979, lowered the crest at Chesilton by 2.5m. Recession can also be fast. Currently it is c.1m every 10 years but the long-term figures suggest that these measurements are often within the inaccuracies of the surveys used and may be a local feature. The beach is trying to swing away from Chesilton into Weymouth Bay but this is most apparent in times of storm activity (Carr and Seaward 1990, 1991).

The most dramatic effects are seen in storms when great cusps develop in the beach face. This has the effect of concentrating flow into the hollows to give a maximum height of water on the beach. Sometimes this then allows overwash. It also forms a beautiful pump so that the high levels of water in the beach, overlying the pebbles with sand matrix, are pumped through the beach to emerge, forcibly, on the inland side. Overwash may be related to the production of the hollows on the landward-side, called 'canns'. On the seaward face there is a regular spacing of hollows called cusps, the spacing of which is in turn a function of the swash zone sediment transfer conditions.

There is an incomplete knowledge of the sediment system but the consensus of available measurements and calculations has shown that there is a net eastward transport, certainly as far as Wyke Regis. There is a more variable transport at Portland with no net accumulation. This agrees with the observation that there is no continuing build-up or loss offshore at this point. The direction of drift does change with time. The wave climate seemed to change in 1982 with more south-westerly storms and fewer easterlies. The calculations of drift for West Bay showed a net westward drift of c.8000m³ a year between 1974 and 1982 and a net eastward drift of 14 000m³ a year afterwards.

During 1995-96 this has again reversed. The apparent net westward drift at West Bay shown by the supposed accumulation of sediment on the eastern side of the piers is probably an illusion. It is, of course, the classic indicator of the longshore drift process because it is logical to assume that material is trapped behind a barrier on the updrift side. To operate, however, this requires that the sediment supply system is open, with a continuous supply of sediment, in this case from the landslides of the west Dorset coast. If that supply is cut off as it now is by the rocks and slides below Golden Cap and Thorncombe Beacon and there is a long-term net loss to the east the western side will diminish. The eastern side will be maintained for a time by the flow from the west but when the supply is exhausted the eastern side will also begin to lower and retreat. Of course, this is capable of short-term reversal. At West Bay, and all the way from Lyme Regis, for example, the long-term trend can be demonstrated by historical photographs to have existed at least from 1824 to 1974 with fast erosion in 1961-64. Between 1974 and 1982 there may have been a reversal of the trend due to more easterlies, if we can trust the numerical models used, but **for the period 1982-93 there has been massive erosion on the eastern side and virtually no supply from the west.** The piers for the old Bridport sewer pipe, which was laid at beach level, stood 2m proud above the beach in 1994, and beach feeding, bringing material back from Burton Bradstock by lorry, has now been started. It is important that these facts are recognised by the engineers responsible for the new marina proposals at West Bay. It would be a pity if the installation made the existing fragile system even more vulnerable.

There seems to be little doubt that Chesil Beach is in a fragile state. It is finite in amount. No more material is being supplied and loss continues through attrition and burial offshore. The logical prediction must be that Chesil Beach will now steadily lower, move onshore and break up into separate beaches and bays. It will rotate at Weymouth, breach at several places and the Fleet will become saline and then disappear or develop into lakes like those behind Cogden and West Bexington. The main new headland will be at the Narrows. Severe erosion will take place at East Cliff and Burton Bradstock, where the next bays will develop. The processes which happen when a barrier beach comes onshore, already seen between Lyme Regis and West Bay, will be the model for the rest of the beach.

Beach management

This has very important implications for beach management at the eastern end. Of course the timescales are quite long and it should not be assumed that there is immediate or even medium-term risk for the main bulk of Chesil Beach, but there are already problems at Chesilton and there is public concern. For example the *Western Gazette* of 15 February 1990 ran the headline 'Coast in Peril as beach is battered' and went on to describe how the beach could be breached at any time:

'Whatever the reason for it, the storms are certainly more frequent, and we seem to get extra high tides regularly. There is no doubt the sea-level is rising. I believe the beach has moved more in the past 20 years than in the previous 300-400 years and is weakening,'

said the flood bailiff. This is a predictable immediate reaction to a major event which demonstrates public feeling. The official response was more restrained. The Borough Engineer felt that 'the equilibrium would return' and the National River Authority works engineer seemed to be tempting fate with, 'If the material does not come back in time then it will be the first time ever.'

The reality is that flooding has occurred many times, the most famous in 1824 when 26 people drowned and 80 houses were damaged or destroyed. Since then there have been 22 events of concern and an occasion in 1936 when King George V was stranded! The events which caused public action were the storm of 13 December 1978 with strong persistent onshore winds, and the ocean swell of 13 February 1979 when 18-second period waves arrived without warning out of a moderate sea. The 1978 event was a 5-year, 6.5m storm surge flood and the 1979 event was a 50-year, 9m ocean swell flood. The human response to these events was a sea defence scheme, designed by Dobbie and Partners for Wessex Water Authority. The scheme was completed in 1988 and consisted of a trial beach crest stabilisation using gabion mattresses, modifications to the sea-wall, an increase to the level of the road and a massive gallery to drain the beach. This system is a flexible and imaginative attempt to handle a very difficult environmental situation. It performed well in a storm of 16 December 1989 but needed heavy remedial works. A noticeable effect was that the gabion mattresses settled at a steep angle. This might cause problems in the future because it has the effect of producing a vertical wall. This may increase scour and cause collapse of the whole system. As with most things on Chesil Beach it seems that we will only find out in time and by trial and error!

Viewpoints and access

There are two famous viewpoints which provide magnificent general panoramas of Chesil Beach and its setting. The first is on the Burton Bradstock to Abbotsbury road (B3157) at Wears Hill near Abbotsbury Castle Fort (SY 555866). The second is at the monument at Verne Yeates on the Isle of Portland (SY 688730). At both localities there is a good car park.

Easy access to the beach for coaches is at West Bay, Bridport (SY 464903), and along the causeway from Weymouth to Portland (where there are various large car parks). More limited access, suitable only for cars and minibuses, is available at Burton Bradstock (SY 487890), West Bexington (SY 534865), and Abbotsbury (SY 560846). The remedial works are best visited from the car parks opposite to the entrance to the Naval base.

GLOSSARY

Aquiclude A rock formation which may be porous and contain water but which is not significantly permeable, and so helps to control the movement of water in adjacent permeable aquifers lying above and below it.

Cambering Where rock strata adjoining a valley overlie clay, the elastic nature of the clay causes the overlying rocks to sag towards the valley, producing a convex profile to the hilltop.

Chert Layers or irregular concretions of silica occurring, usually, in limestone and sandy formations.

Graben A valley or trough produced by faulting and subsidence or by uplift of adjacent rock masses (Horsts).

Head A deposit similar to Coombe Rock in origin but formed on bedrocks other than chalk. Also a coastal headland.

Isometric A drawing of a three dimensional object, without perspective, so that equal lengths along the three axes are drawn equal.

Kaolinite A clay mineral, consisting mainly of hydrated aluminium silicate, produced by the weathering of rock minerals such as feldspars. Common mineral in tropical weathering profiles.

Laterite An iron-rich weathering zone produced particularly in the tropics by rigorous chemical selection where conditions favour greater mobility of silica than of iron.

Lithology The general character of a rock, particularly as seen in field exposures and hand specimens.

Mesozoic A collective term for the span of time from the Triassic to the Cretaceous.

Pericline A dome produced by folding of rock strata. An anticline which pitches at both ends.

Periglacial The zone surrounding or bordering the glacial zone and one in which frost action is important.

Sarsen See silcrete.

Scree An accumulation of mainly angular material which lies at an angle of about 35° beneath an exposed cliff or free face. The principal cause of deposition is rock-fall.

Silcrete A highly siliceous indurated material formed at or near the earth's surface by the silicification of bedrock, weathering products or other deposits.

Solifluction The wholesale movement, in cold regions, of an upper, wet (thawed) layer of material over frozen or otherwise impermeable ground.

Tertiary The first part or period of the Cainozoic (Cenozoic) era, comprising the Palaeocene through to the Pliocene. It was followed by the Quaternary.

Unconformable Denoting the relationship between one rock body and another laid down on top of it. The classic unconformity is that where a series of dipping strata has been planed off by erosion and later strata have been laid down on top. The later strata have a recognisably different angle of dip.

BIBLIOGRAPHY

Allison, R.J. and Brunsden, D. (1990) 'Some mudslide movement patterns' in *Earth Surface Processes and Landforms*, 15, 297-311.

Allison, R.J. (ed) (1992) *The Coastal Landforms of West Dorset, Geologists' Association Guide no 47*. The Geologists' Association, London, 134. This is an alternative guide to the coast with articles by Allison, R.J. (Introduction Geology, Landslide Types and Processes, Higher Sea Lane); Koh, A. (Black Ven); Rudkin, H. (Stonebarrow); Bray, M. (Coastal Sediment Supply and Transport, Chesil Beach); Lee, E.M. (Urban Landslides). It is a development of Allison, R.J. (1990) 'Landslides of the Dorset coast', in *British Geomorphological Research Group, Field Guide*. 128.

Arber, M.A. (1941) 'The coastal landslips of west Dorset' *in Proceedings of the Geologists' Association*, 52, 273-83.

Arber, M.A. (1973) 'Landslips near Lyme Regis' in *Proceedings of the Geologists' Association*, 84, 121-33.

Bird, E.C.F. (1989) 'The beaches of Lyme Bay' in *Proceedings of the Dorset Natural History and Archaeological Society*, 111, 91-7.

Bray, M.J. (1992) 'Coastal sediment supply and transport' in Allison, R.J. (ed) *The Coastal Landforms of West Dorset*, 94-118.

Brunsden, D. (1969) 'The moving cliffs of Black Ven' in *Geography Magazine*, 41, 5, 372-4.

Brunsden, D. (1973) 'The application of systems theory to the study of mass movement' in *Geologica Applicata e Idrogeologia[DJW9]*, 8, 185-207.

Brunsden, D. (1974) 'The degradation of a coastal slope, Dorset, England' in Brown, E.H. and Waters, R.S. (eds) in *Progress in Geomorphology (Special Publication no. 7)*. London: Institute of British Geographers, 79-98.

Brunsden, D. and Goudie, A. (1981) *Landform Guides No 1: Classic coastal landforms of Dorset*. The Geographical Association and the British Geomorphological Research Group.

Brunsden, D. and Jones, D.K.C (1972) 'The morphology of degraded landslide slopes in south-west Dorset' in *Quarterly Journal of Engineering Geology*, 5, 205-22.

Brunsden, D. and Jones, D.K.C. (1976) 'The evolution of landslide slopes in Dorset' in *Philosophical Transactions of the Royal Society of London*, Series A, 283, 605-31.

Brunsden, D. and Jones, D.K.C. (1980) 'Relative time scales and formative events in coastal landslide systems' in *Zeitschrift fur Geomorphologie*, 34, 1-19.

Carr, A.P. and Seaward, D.R. (1990) 'Chesil Beach: changes in crest height 1969-1990' in *Proceedings of the Dorset Natural History and Archaeological Society*, 112, 109-12.

Carr, A.P. and Seaward, D.R. (1991) 'Chesil Beach: landward reunion 1965-1991' in *Proceedings of the Dorset Natural History and Archaeological Society*, 113, 157-60.

Carter, R.W.G. (1989) 'Rising sea level' in *Geology Today*, 5, 63-7.

Chandler, J.H. and Brunsden, D. (1995) 'Steady state behaviour of the Black Ven mudslide: the application of archival analytical photogrammetry to study of landform change' in *Earth Surface Process and Landforms*, 20, 255-75.

Conway, B.W. (1974) 'The Black Ven landslip, Charmouth, Dorset', Institute of Geological Sciences, *NERC Report No. 74/3*.

Conway, B.W. (1979) 'The contribution made to cliff instability by head deposits in the west Dorset coastal area' in *Quarterly Journal of the Geological Society*, 12, 267-79.

Davies, G.M. (1956) *The Dorset Coast: A geological guide* (second edition). London: Black.

Denness, B., Conway, B.W., McCann, D.M. and Grainger, P. (1975) 'Investigation of a coastal landslip at Charmouth, Dorset' in *Quarterly Journal of Engineering Geology*, 8, 119-40.

Fairbridge, R.W. (1961) 'Eustatic changes in sea-level' in *Physics and Chemistry of the Earth*, 4, 99-185.

Fowles, J. (1991) *A Short History of Lyme Regis*. Dovercote Press, Dorset.

House, M. (1989) *Geology of the Dorset Coast*. London: Geologists' Association.

Isaac, K.P. (1981) 'Tertiary weathering profiles in the plateau deposits of east Devon' in *Proceedings of the Geologists' Association*, 92, 159-68.

Isaac, K.P. (1983) 'Tertiary lateritic weathering in Devon, England and the Palaeogene continental environment of southwest England' in *Proceedings of the Geologists' Association*, 94, 105-15.

Lang, W.D. (1914) 'The geology of the Charmouth cliffs, beach and foreshore' in *Proceedings of the Geologists' Association*, 25, 293-360.

Lang, W.D. (1942) 'Geological notes, 1941-1942' in *Proceedings of the Natural History and Archaeological Society*, 64, 129-30. Also in *Geological Notes* (1944), 66, 129.

Langridge, G.A. (1980) 'Relationship between wave energy and coastal landsliding, Dorset Coast' unpublished undergraduate dissertation, Kings College, 58.

Morner, N.A. (1968) 'The late Quaternary history of the Kattegatt Sea and the Swedish west coast' in *Sveriges Geologiska Undersokning*, Series C, NR 640, Arsbok 63, NR 3.

Perkins, W.J. (1977) *Geology Explained in Dorset*. David and Charles, Newton Abbot.

Rudkin, H.L. (1992) 'Stonebarrow Hill' in Allison, R.J. (ed) *The Coastal Landforms of West Dorset*. Geologists' Association, 50-61.

Shennan, I. (1989) 'Holocene coastal movements and sea level changes in Great Britain' in *Journal of Quaternary Science*, 4, 77-89.

Shepard, F.P. (1963) 'Thirty-five thousand years of sea-level' in Clements, T. (ed) *Essays in Marine Geology in Honor of K.O. Emery*. California University Press, Los Angeles. 1-10.

Waters, R.S. (1960) 'The bearing of superficial deposits on the age and origin of the upland plain of east Devon, west Dorset and south Somerset' in *Transactions of the Institute of British Geographers*, 28, 89-97.

Wilson, V., Welch, F.B.A., Robbie, J.A. and Green, G.W. (1958) 'Geology of the country around Bridport and Yeovil (Sheets 327 and 312)' in *Memoirs of the Geological Survey of Great Britain*. London: HMSO.